and the unenviable responsibility of the decisions that they have to take. We had a lot of fun listening to tales of their triumphs and mishaps, and gradually we became used to watching the more unsightly scenes and operations . . . we just kept on snapping! But for the sake of the more squeamish, many of these photographs have been omitted from the book. The ones we included are comparatively tame.

Ennis Bentham is but one of many women whom we have seen hard at work on their hill farms. In order to show the varied and consistent contribution that women make throughout the year, we decided it would be more appropriate to work with one shepherdess instead of many. The more time we spent with Ennis, the more we realised the unstinting effort she puts into the running of the hill farm. Nothing daunted her and jokes never failed, while unending care was lavished on the animals. It is through her family and farm-work that her happiness and fulfilment are found.

Photographing the children was simply a question of spending time with them and being ready for the unexpected. They were intrigued by our medium-format cameras, and we encouraged their interest, letting them look through the lens and decide what they thought would make a good picture. We liked them to be involved with the project – even though on occasion we missed shots because they were carrying the cameras! What impressed us was not only the amount of responsibility that children take at a relatively early age, but also their skill and confidence in handling the stock. We would like to say a special thankyou to all the children of Dent Primary School for helping us with the text for this story. Their tales succinctly put into words what we had seen for ourselves on the farms.

We would also like to thank the four Dales vets, David Metcalfe, Adam Hurn, Nick Preston and Ian Robinson, for all their time, explanations, hospitality and numerous telephone calls, both day and night, when interesting jobs came up. Since the completion of the project Ian Robinson has left the practice to further his interests in working with wildlife; he now manages a seal sanctuary for the R.S.P.C.A.

Our thanks also go out to the Richardsons at Watendlath and the Benthams of Deepdale. Both families made us feel welcome and at home during the many days we spent with them. We followed them on sheep gathers, did the rounds with them at lambing, became accustomed to their daily routine of 'doing-up' the cattle and feeding the sheep, and enjoyed the seasonal variety of the work at dipping, clipping, or tupping-time. Without their support it would not have been possible to make this book.

Documenting the lives of folk who live among the fells, depends as much upon their co-operation as upon our ability to photograph them. They are wonderful people to work with, and it is a privilege to spend our days in their company. They are the kind of folk that restore one's faith in humanity . . . LIFE IN THE HILLS is dedicated to them.

Our thanks also go to Evelyn Sinclair for the time and care she has taken with the design work, Richard David, Eliza's father, for the work he has done in editing the text, and James Marsden from English Nature.

Lastly we would like to pay a special tribute to our publisher, Colin Baker, who not only gives us the encouragement to explore our ideas freely, but also the support to see them through. LIFE IN THE HILLS could not have been made without his help.

John & Eliza Forder

Much of a vet's time is spent treating cattle and many of the problems tend to revolve around the whole process of reproduction. In other words, his routine requires a lot of 'hand-up-the-bum' work. Firstly, there is getting an unresponsive cow into calf, then confirming it is in calf, possible emergencies just before calving such as milk fever, the calving itself, and then 'cow cleansings', prolapses and mastitis – any of which may happen after the birth.

Other jobs include the frequent paring of cows' overgrown hooves, and the treating of any inherent infection. After all half a ton of animal has to walk around on four relatively little feet in a lot of muck and wet.

There are also respiratory ailments and stomach problems such as the 'displaced abomasum' when, owing to paralysis, the true stomach slips onto the wrong side of the cow. This may have to be corrected surgically. Also nails, pieces of wire and sharp stones can occasionally be ingested and become lodged inside the cow causing lesions. If the cow is ailing badly, the vet will decide to operate: this involves delving around inside the stomach amongst thirty to forty gallons of part-digested food, searching for the offending object. In the past, it was always said a wise vet would take along an extra little piece of wire . . . just in case . . . after all he would not have wanted to disappoint the farmer, and the cow invariably improved!

"There's something wonderful about guddling around – squeeze bits here and pummel them there; a bit of berating the intestine well and truly gets the body defences excited!"

The vet is kept busiest with the sheep around lambing time. First he must diagnose and prevent outbreaks of abortion. Next there are the metabolic disorders, such as twin-lamb disease and calcium deficiency, and the problems of lamb-bed necks coming out: then there are the awkward lambings themselves. After lambing, less of the attention goes on the sheep because the lambs have come along with their own numerous and diverse ailments.

For the most part it is the congregating together of animals that increases the risk of illness, so the more intensive the farm, the easier it is for infection to spread. This is especially the case as far as the E. Coli complaints, such as watery mouth and rattlebelly, are concerned. Unless these are treated quickly, they can be fatal, for it is not just the organism itself that causes the problems, but the poisons that are let out into the bloodstream; lambs consequently suffer from enterotoxaemia, or blood-poisoning, and die from severe shock.

But lambs suffer from all sorts of things: there are sauty lambs, 'crambley' lambs, lambs with swayback or dysentery and lambs that are just 'daft'. Some lambs have an 'imperforate anus', in other words, no back passage, and this has to be corrected by making the necessary, little incision. Other lambs have the opposite problem known as 'toffee bum', when their bottoms get all caked up with yellowy, toffee-like muck. However the vets launch a strong educational campaign before lambing-time, and by and large the farmers cope well with the help of periodic advice, a bit of treatment and appropriate supplies of drugs.

The dogs, cats, guinea-pigs, gerbils and budgerigars make a welcome change from the farm animals. Small animal work gives the vet an opportunity to practise much more sophisticated techniques using the latest forms of treatment. For this purpose the surgery contains thousands of pounds worth of equipment ranging from blood biochemistry analysers to X-ray and anaesthetic machinery. The treatment of large animals seems by contrast more like 'bucket and spade work'.

On the whole the Dales vet sees proportionally fewer domestic pets than in town practices, for the simple reason that these animals benefit and thrive from living in the country. Pets are easily stressed and in a city they are usually kept inside, cooped up, and have to cope with an unnatural environment. Behavioural complaints and physical illness often ensue. For the most part, Dales dogs are contented dogs; they like the fells and the fells suit them.

However, some pet owners have problems. An elderly lady, failing to understand that puppies play, will ask for an injection to calm down her one-year-old golden retriever because "it has far too much energy". And a worried poodle owner will complain that his dog never eats a decent meal; the vet discovers later it is fed on three pounds of meat titbits daily.

"Pets benefit from knowing they come second in the pecking order – and a bit of discipline does no harm. We may be able to help the pet, but it's sometimes a question of whether the owner is capable of carrying out the appropriate instructions."

The Dales vets cope with visitors' dogs too.

"One summer I saw three dogs that had injuries from falling down waterfalls – and one of them had gone over Hardraw Force, a hundred foot drop. It had broken its back and was in a hell of a lot of pain. I took one look at it and said 'Awfully sorry . . .' and reached behind me for the bottle. I suppose I misjudged the situation because the owner needed time to come to terms with it. He muttered something about vets reaching for the bottle too soon and . . . anyway, I agreed to sedate it and do some X-rays when I could. I kept it overnight and the poor dog was in so much pain I had to give it more anaesthetic to knock it under. The owner arrived the next day and just said 'Sorry – please, put it to sleep.' He then drove all the way home to Birmingham to bury the dog, came back up again, and the next morning there was a bottle of whisky on the doorstep for me."

Inevitably there are times in veterinary work when, no matter how hard one tries, an animal does not respond to treatment and dies unexpectedly. In these situations it is easy for the vet to feel distressed and to blame himself. Yet, more often than not, the client is full of gratitude and respect for the job he has tried to do. There are other times when an animal makes a miraculous recovery against all odds, and there is not even so much as a 'thank you'.

To many people, the veterinary surgery is like a sanctuary. It is where you take the baby swift, poisoned badger, kestrel with the broken wing, abandoned fox cub or simply the stray kitten. All these end up on the vet's table to be treated, fed and cared for. It is too easy for him to adopt pets.

It is also easy for him to be injured.

"We spend half our life at the back end of cows so there are bound to be dangers; we just have to accept it." There are scars on the hands, bent fingers, bruises, a cracked rib or two and the occasional blow on the head.

"A cow only has to throw her head up unexpectedly and it's as good as an upper cut. I remember thinking . . . there's two of that farmer over there . . . there were two white lines on the road home as well . . ."

It is the quieter cows that the vet needs to watch, the ones the farmer says will be no trouble. It is often they that will lash out and give a short, sharp kick below the knee – and the wellington boots offer little protection. Cows can be tricky but horses and dogs can be trickier, for they are sensitive creatures and pick up feelings easily. A horse also has more potential to do damage as it can kick twice as high, twice as far and in all directions – and there is a bit of metal at the end of its foot.

Over the years the vet has realised that he has to be on his guard constantly to minimise risks. He understands too that the small animals can be as hazardous as the large ones: an infected cat-bite on his hand can just as easily put him in trouble as a painful butt from a cow. And, like the farmer, the vet just has to carry on working – pain or no pain. But whatever the injury it is important that he does not lose his nerve. If a heifer turns on him while he is trying to calve her, he may well feel uneasy when facing the next few cows; but he knows he has to regain his confidence quickly, otherwise it would be impossible for him to be among the animals, grabbing hold of them, working with them and trying to make them better.

As the vet learns to cope with the dangers of his trade, he also begins to understand the vagaries of the Dales weather. Whether it is rain driving up from the valley bottoms, gales, a hot sultry summer's day or a white-out on the tops, the vet has to do his rounds. If a cow needs seeing at some inaccessible farm out on the fell, and heavy snowfalls have made the roads impassable, the Dales vet will do everything he can to get there. But it is easy for him to be misled. Down in the village there need be hardly a trace of snow and yet, as soon as height is gained there is a thick enough covering to make the terrain unrecognizable. Few realise the persistent force that drives the snow across the fell, concealing the familiar landmarks, leaving only faint indentations where walls have been and reducing telegraph poles to the size of fence posts. There is little respite as, out on the open fell, relentless winds drive the snow into deep drifts and, within minutes of a clearing having been made, it is covered again.

The maintenance of the fell roads cannot be a priority for the council, for until the snow ceases and the winds drop there is little point in clearing them. The vet's good fortune occurs when the winter is mild; then the snow-ploughs and gritters are more available, because they are not needed in the market towns and along the valley bottoms, and the vet can put in a special request.

"I need to see a cow at Fleet Moss. Can I have some help?"
Before too long the vet's Land Rover is setting off accompanied by the snow-plough, a J.C.B. and the gritter. With the digger digging, the snow-plough working at full pelt and the salt from the gritter doing its best to counteract the freezing conditions, a wide enough pathway is made to get the Land Rover through. However, after an hour or so the fell top tells the familiar tale – snow has blown in and succeeded in obliterating the road again.
"Good thing we didn't leave you to it", the driver of the snow-plough chuckled, "you'd have been spending t' night up here!" The council men were no longer surprised at the speed at which their work was undone.

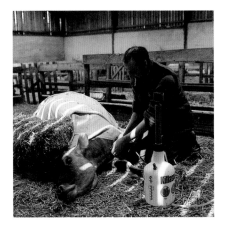

For travelling in winter is as much about getting back as it is about getting there. Even when the fell road has been negotiated there is no guarantee that the return journey will be safe.
"I thought it wasn't too bad . . . I was on my way to Kettlewell and coming over Kidstones it was a complete and utter white-out. I couldn't make anything out and off I went straight into a snow drift and got stuck – stuck in my Vauxhall Viva. The snow eased off a bit so I walked down into Cray to get help, but in the twenty minutes it took me to get down the blizzard had become so fierce we couldn't get back out again. It was night time before I got going; I ended up going sixty miles round by Harrogate to get back home."

It is not just the cold and snow that impedes the vet; the heat and midges can make life difficult too. When it is hot it can seem unbearable to don the protective clothing, and a compromise has to be made between keeping cool and keeping clean. Either the vet stifles and sweats beneath his oversuit and keeps clean, or else he strips off and gets mucked up. In other words it's about "sweating like a pig, or looking like one!"

It does not matter. It is a part of his life. To be a Dales vet is to live and work in a small community and to provide them with a service twenty-four hours a day. That is what he enjoys and that is what he believes in. It is the unexpected nature of the work that keeps him on his toes.

Difficult decisions often have to be made on the spur of the moment, and without full knowledge of the facts. Can he pull the calf out or is it going to be a caesar? These are the grey areas, when he would like to save the farmer expense by 'doing a pull', but the size of a calf is never certain. How can he possibly tell from a head and two hooves that the calf's behind is not like a hippopotamus? It is only afterwards that the vet is in a position to justify or regret his decision. Whenever possible he likes to be able to spend time with his clients explaining the symptoms and relating the consequences of every option, for he views consultation as an essential part of his work.

The education of farmers in basic veterinary procedures is in their own interest. The vet's holding of discussion evenings before lambing-time and tupping-time enables him to pass on reminders of general health care and warn of ominous signs to watch out for. Farmers can then recognise the difference between ailments they can treat themselves and those for which they need help. The 20-year-old bottle of brown drench that used to be the 'cure-all' has been finally set aside in favour of modern methods.

Although the Dales vet emphasises the benefits of preventative medicine, farmers are busy people and the mundane jobs such as paring feet and de-horning get postponed for the sunny days – and there are never enough of them! Then suddenly there's the urgent request, "Fix this tup for tomorrow please!" And so one phone call just before the vet sets out on his rounds throws the whole day's plan into chaos.

Dalesfolk are hard-working, uncomplicated characters who are content with little and are always willing to help. If the vet needs an extra man to roll a cow over, they will happily go and seek him, even if they only return with the 80-year-old neighbour.
"So this is your hired muscle is it?" The vet laughs, but between them they all cope.

The life of a Dales vet is spent treating and consulting; he will assist the farmers in whatever way he can. But he also allows time for idle chatter, drinking tea and eating a good spread. He is a part of the community. Each day brings with it that element of newness and uncertainty.

It is past eleven at night and, as the vet sips his drink and reminisces, he concludes, "I've no idea what will happen, not even in the next three minutes." As he speaks, the phone rings . . .

"The vet views consultation as an essential part of his work"
David gives advice about a poorly tup – Swaledale

A case of summer mastitis:
Adam, with help from the farmer, rolls the cow over in order
to examine the udder – Wensleydale

Ian examines a crush injury in the surgery

Adam pares an over-grown hoof to relieve a cow of lameness

Scrubbing up

Hosing down

"Back-end work"
Adam replaces a prolapsed uterus – 6am Wensleydale

Some back-ends are more dangerous than others!
Nick takes a blood sample from the tail vein of a bull

"Fertility rites" – Ian inserts a hormonal coil to stimulate ovulation

A reluctant patient

Tools of the trade

The car boot

Whatever the weather, the vet has to do his rounds

An awkward lambing

The sheep is unconcerned as, under local anaesthetic,
a caesarean is performed to save both mother and lamb

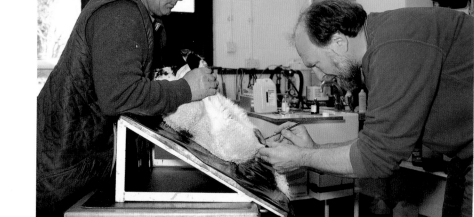

David rectifies an imperforate anus – "a no-back-passage job"

Not every lamb can be saved

Routine work of de-horning

An anxious moment as a case of pneumonia is diagnosed

Ian treats a wounded swan whose nest had been vandalised

The only surviving cygnet

"The vet's surgery is a sanctuary"

A Gloucester Old Spot with farrowing fever

Horse dentistry

David and Adam castrate a colt – Wensleydale

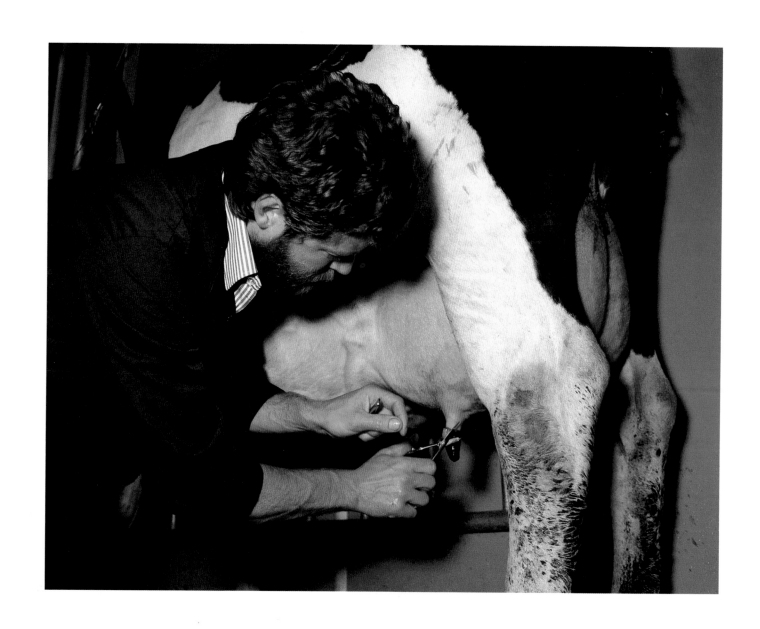

Casualty work – Adam stitches up a torn teat

David administers an intravenous antidote to a stirk suffering from lead-poisoning

A case of milk-fever:
"The vet pulled her tail, the dog barked hopefully
and the cow unsteadily got to her feet"

"Have a nip o' rum in your tea – does you a world o' good"

WATENDLATH

A High Lakeland Farm

Blea Tarn

There is something alluring about the approach to Watendlath. A narrow road winds its way sharply up through Ashness Wood, where oak and birch trees seem to be protecting the secluded valley that lies beyond them. Unexpectedly the woodland ceases and, ahead, two imposing crags stand as a gateway to a dale that somehow seems more like alpine pasture than a part of England. As the beck is followed up for a mile or so, stone walls criss-cross the gentler meadow land and the eye is led up toward a group of buildings and an ancient pack-horse bridge, a reminder that the valley has served the needs of other generations. The few houses, byres and barns nestle together, and almost shield from view the central feature of the dale itself – Watendlath Tarn. Beyond this the land rises up to the dale-head; and, as the shepherd looks back, this familiar patch of water provides reassurance that there lies home.

The upper reaches of Watendlath have a sense of wildness about them.
"It is open to the four winds."
This expanse of fell, rising to two and a half thousand feet, is wide open to the elements and offers little protection from the weather that blows in across the hills. Driving rain, sleet and snow come in quick succession and on this upland there are few peaks or crags to offer shelter. Shallow hollows on either side of the valley conceal two more tarns. A few surrounding hillocks provide partial protection to Dock Tarn on the western side, while Blea Tarn over to the east feels more exposed. To the intruder it can seem an untamed place.

Yet, when the sun's rays break through the overhanging cloud and the light wind stirs the grasses, all sense of desolation disappears. Each contour and detail of the fell is illuminated, and a myriad shapes and patterns emerge. The varying colours of the mosses and the heather, the coarse fell grasses, and the dark outcrops of rock, blend together to create a gentle patchwork of soft yellows and grey-greens. The land, that at first appeared featureless, takes on a strange beauty of its own and any feeling of bleakness is at once dispelled. The vastness of the fell, the closeness of the skies serve to uplift and inspire, and not to overawe.

The shepherd knows this. This is his home and this is where he belongs – out here on the high fell. A tiny figure in the landscape, crook in hand and dogs at his side, he steadily works his way up toward the fell fence at Ullscarf.

Here, five times a year, he will come to gather his sheep, turn them round, and drive them home along the well-worn path between the brackens to the intakes at the farm.

As he sets out, he skirts along the edge of his land, stopping every now and again to chivvy stray sheep on up the fell. Momentarily he becomes absorbed by the splendour of the surrounding hills, and notices beneath him the comparative lushness of the adjoining dales. By contrast, the land at Watendlath starts at nearly a thousand feet and there are no flat lambing fields here. His inside land is literally 'intake' land – pieces of land that have been taken and fenced off from the fell. Yet, as the shepherd does the rounds of his stock each day, he acknowledges that his valley has a richness and rarity of its own. He will never tire of it: he knows that his work and his happiness lie here.

Watendlath Tarn

But for how long? There are records of sheep having been farmed in Watendlath since the twelfth century, and the present landscape stands as a testimony to those who have cared for it in the past. Fold Head Farm is situated close by Watendlath Tarn, and the holding comprises three thousand acres of fell land. Not long ago as many as nine men used to work that land: now there are only two, and it is a struggle for the farm to provide a living for them.
"There's a lot to care for if you're ganna do t' job properly. The maintenance is astronomical. Tek stone-walling for instance . . . Ah tell ye, if all t' wall gaps were up in Watendlath this very night – not a stone off anywhere – a man could start work 'ere tomorrow morning, and be kept in a full time job doing nowt else but walling. And that's what it would tek to keep t' walls reet here."

It is not an easy life. But those who work at Watendlath are not there for that.
"To t' old folk, money meant nowt 'cos nay-body had any – everybody was t' same. It's different now . . . there's plenty mair of it abut. T' men and womenfolk in Borrowdale 'ave allus known it hard. Not long back, women would gar abut in low-top clogs wi' coarse brats fastened round themselves – like aprons they were. In them they'd put kindlin' for t' fire. And in t' evening men would just sit round t' fire on hard, straight-backed chairs, an' smoake their pipes, spit in t' fire, an' t' wireless was only put on for t' nine o'clock news. There was nay entertainment. Sole topic of conversation was fox-hunting an' sheep, 'cos that was their life. And it was so bloody cold like – a great, big,

black-leaded range with nobbut a few red cinders in't, and t' old chap wouldn't allow a lump o' coal to be put on t' fire after eight o'clock. Bed-time was when t' candle burned."

Dick Richardson was born in 1935, and was brought up on High Lodore Farm in Borrowdale. At fifteen he started working as a shepherd near to home, but fell farms rarely had the means to keep their labour all the year round, so hired hands would have to move on in winter, and find work on the lowland farms around Penrith and Cockermouth. "Ah was allus a bit of a wanderer. But ye 'ad to be to survive."

After two years with the army doing his national service, Dick decided to seek more stable work in the slate quarries. But handling slate is not the same as handling sheep; he soon grew restless and decided to return to farmwork. However it is difficult for a young man to make a living from fell farming, good enough to keep himself and his young wife. Either he needs to own his own farm – which is unusual in Lakeland – or have sufficient funds to rent one and stock it with sheep.

"Well, t' wages in casual farmwork wouldn't keep a hen. So off Ah went to work on t' excavator building M 6 – and Ah worked eight year on that. It was lang hours, and at night Ah used to sleep out – in me van, in tents, underneath t' digger between tracks . . . Ah could sleep on a clothes-line Ah could. Mind, ye could earn good money there. But it never felt reet, Ah allus wanted to git back to farming."

In 1970 Dick got a job working for the National Trust as an estate worker. He and his family moved to Watendlath, where Margaret, his wife, ran a tea-shop, while Dick worked for the Trust during winter, and in the summer months did contract work – walling, clipping and any other farm jobs he could find. It was another nine years before the Richardsons had the opportunity of taking over the holding by the tarn – Fold Head Farm. At last, after many years of trying for farms, they had their own place leased from the National Trust, for whom they have always had the highest regard as landlords. Dick's great-uncles had farmed at Watendlath, and Dick had often worked it: now he was to run Fold Head himself, with the help of his eldest son, Shaun. He knew those fells like the back of his hand and he was glad to be there.

It is a father and son team. Although Shaun tends to do more of the hard, physical work, they each turn their hand to what is needed at any particular time. They have an easy working relationship, helped by their sense of humour and genial good nature . . . though Dick remembers the times Shaun calls him a "fly bugger"! They both share the same enthusiasm and willingness to pitch in and make the farm work against difficult odds. But equally they know how to stop off and enjoy a good crack. When friends call, they are well rewarded. The kettle is put on, coffee is made, good stories are told and what was to be a ten minute chat easily becomes a few hours. The Richardsons' hospitality is as much a part of their nature, as Watendlath is an integral part of their lives.

Herdwick, Swaledale and Cheviot sheep are all kept on the holding, but there is no doubt that the Herdwicks, which are the hardy Lakeland breed, survive best on those fells. They manage throughout the winter with no extra fodder and can last for as long as three weeks buried in snow: if there is a dead sheep found, it is more likely to be a Swaledale. Indeed, the type of stock that is kept must be a prime consideration among the Lakeland fells, for one of the main problems that the farmer faces is the unpredictability of the weather.

Tip-time

"It can be rough, very rough. Ye can have tremendous winters up 'ere. Ah've known it when snow blaws in and comes up to t' spoutin's on t' house. T' whole valley looks just like a desert, all white, wid walls all gone and just trees sticking out. Very pretty mind! At times tarn can git frozen over mair than twenty inches thick so that we can fetch sheep across it. They're not so keen o' coming across mind, 'cos they still think it's water. We leave fell gyats open, but in a bad storm t' sheep are blown in at t' back o' fell wall, and git buried in all them dips. T' dogs find them mind, but they can be twenty foot or mair deep. We've had sheep buried at tip-time and sheep buried at lambing. Trouble is ye just never know what's goin' to be thrown at ye next."

It is not just the sheep that get into trouble. Walkers can be caught out too. When there are blizzard conditions and a white-out on the fell, the only chance people have of finding their way down is to follow the walls and fences.
"It's t' only safe way to come down. When ye can't see owt, some of them peat bogs up there can be terrible dangerous – ground's like quick-sand. And ye

can't follow gills, 'cos ye'd come down o'er t' waterfalls. Follow t' walls and fences, they'll allus come down to a wall, then another wall or a fence, or summat." For it has happened that on the threshold of Fold Head Farm there have turned up bedraggled and frozen souls, numbed senseless by the cold, in need of warmth and sustenance to thaw them out. Nevertheless, a bit of snow or dry cold is preferable to the constant rain and wind.

"When t' wind blows for week after week, whistlin' round t' farmhouse, it begins to git to ye. But sleet, that's the worst, cold sleet . . . oooh . . . that's a corker. Serious like. Mind, whatever the weather, Ah allus sleep wid t' windows wide open, summer or winter. Ah've had snow on t' bed, and snow on me long johns in t' morning."

Lambing starts on the first of April for the half-bred sheep, and a month later for the fell sheep. With no lambing sheds and very few flat fields, lambing takes place in the intakes. However, as the sheep are not confined they are able to go off among the trees or behind rocks and lamb by themselves. To the shepherd this seems a more natural environment. In wet and stormy weather, it is not difficult for them to find shelter among the heather and, as they are out in the open, infection does not easily spread. Diseases such as watery-mouth and rattlebelly are not prevalent.

The biggest danger to the lambs comes from crows, magpies and foxes. Crows will peck lambs' eyes out even while the sheep are giving birth, and a fox may be responsible for taking as many as fifty lambs during the season. It is a substantial loss, and one that cannot be afforded. Shaun may cover up to twenty miles a day checking on the sheep and making sure that the new lambs are fit and have a belly full of milk. Meanwhile 'Doctor Dick' remains near the farmstead and deals with any emergencies that are brought back to him. He nurses the sickly ones, mothers on the orphans and ensures that any starved lambs are properly 'suckled up'.

It is the busiest time of year and the hours are long. Before five in the morning, Dick can be seen leaving the farmhouse to do his first round of the day. With his dog at his side, he quietly paces the fields around the tarn, checking on the ewes, and occasionally stopping for a smoke while he scans the fellside for any problems. At moments like these, he feels pride and contentment in his work. "Nowt ever gits me down, Ah'm not that sort o' person. This is where me happiness is . . . just working here at Watendlath."

At clipping time, with nearly two and half thousand sheep to take the wool off, contract workers are usually brought in to help with the hoggs and the shearlings; these sheep are then sent straight back to the fell. Meanwhile the breeding ewes are kept in the intakes, so that Dick and Shaun can clip a few at a time. The lambs need dosing, dipping and lug-marking as well. The plan is to start clipping in the middle of June, and have it all done by the first of August. When it is hot, the back aches and the sweat pours, but no job that involves working amongst the sheep is ever resented. There is always a sense of deep satisfaction at the end of the day, when well over a hundred sheep have been clipped or dipped.

Summer passes by, the silage is baled up, Watendlath fills and empties with tourists, and when the last of the Lakeland shows is done and the accompanying festivities are over it is time to go back to the fell and gather in the sheep for tip-time.

Lug-marking

"We loose tips on t' first of December, when t' tips start smelling strang and t' yows start flapping their tails abut. We keep near on fifty tips altogether, and run three to a hundred ewes; but a good Swaledale can easily tek a hundred for himself – jammy bugger. We raddle tips for t' first ten days, and as lang as we don't gather them up, tips'll find their own lot o' yows and stay wid 'em. That way we have nay fighting.
"Mind, ye can have problems though. T' other day we fetched a new Cheviot tip back from Hexham and put it amongst some Herdwick yows: next thing we knew it had tipped yan and t' yow had deead. What a deeath! Ah suppose t' yow must have had a heart attack or summat. Another time, we let a tip out of t' byre to run wi' some yows across t' packhorse bridge. Now tips can be very fresh when ye first let 'em loose, over-excited like . . . Anyway it found yan a-tipping, but t' yow jumped up on top of t' bridge wall, tip followed after it, tipped it, and they both rolled o'er into t' beck. Bloody hell . . . Ah couldn't believe me eyes!"

Days off are spent at the shows, tip fairs and shepherds' meets: when there's a get-together the conversation is invariably centred on sheep, with a seasonal flavour according to the time of year. So, in tip-time, farmers will quiz each other appropriately.

"What sort o' tips are you garn to use?"

"Is that tip working alreet?"

"Nay . . . that bugger there can't tip."

"How much did ye give for that yan?"

"By Gad, that's dear."

"And that bloody tip o'er there is nay good."

"But that 'un – have ye ever seen sek a fine Herdwick tip?"

To survive on a fell farm in the Lake District, where the ground is rough and the sheep are lean, is no easy task. Some form of extra income is vital, and many farmers have to rely on tourists for that. Fold Head Farm is a family concern and Dick's wife, Margaret, plays a vital role in contributing to the household economy. Brought up on a farm herself in the Cheviot hills, she now spends her time running a busy bed and breakfast trade. Without her support it is doubtful whether the farm would be viable, and her dedication to the business does not go unrecognised. She gives dinner, bed and breakfast to an unpredictable number of visitors, relying on only one weekly shopping trip to Keswick. Living at Watendlath, Margaret has had to learn to be well organised.

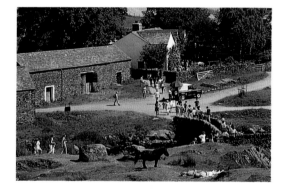

Visitors come to Watendlath from all over Britain, and on a fine summer's day the valley can seem as though it has been taken over by off-comers. The intrusion does not bother the Richardsons; having lived in Borrowdale all their lives, they have been brought up with it and accept it graciously. The bed and breakfasters offer a change of company. They bring in fresh ideas, share news and show a genuine interest in the running of the farm. If they ask questions, Dick takes trouble in answering them.

"After all, what if Ah went down to their place o' work? Ah wouldn't larn owt if Ah didn't ask."

Inevitably, there are a few persistent tourists who believe they know best. Some walkers will actually carry lambs back to the farmhouse from the fell just because they are 'blairing'.

"Well there are hundreds of lambs blairing, and that yan they've brought down off t' fell will have nay chance of finding its mother again." When this happens, they make the walker take the wretched lamb back to the fell, and leave it where they found it. That's its best hope.

With tourists coming and going during the summer season, one of the greatest drawbacks of living at Watendlath is the narrow road with awkward passing places. Because the place is inaccessible, not many traders bother coming up with farm supplies, and when Dick needs to take his sheep to market the problems of getting out of the dale are enough to try the patience of a saint. Dick remembers that once it took him over two hours to make the six mile journey to Keswick – it was a hot day and he had fifty sheep in his trailer.
"When you meet some folk they just sit in t' cars, look at you, and do nowt. They don't know how to use t' full road."

Awkward visitors, the road, cold sleet, or a hungry fox, are but transient difficulties, and rarely over-shadow the pleasure the family derives from living and working there. Their fragile existence is woven from different strands, and each one needs to be nurtured carefully. The upland sheep, the suckler cows, the visitors all play their part; but Watendlath also has another asset besides these – its unique ecology.

From the heather fells and bog areas on the fell tops, to the gills and patches of woodland down below, the dale abounds with a variety of plants. In the past the whole valley would have been covered with trees, but now there are few examples of aged oaks and sycamores. Gradually, over many years, the rearing of stock for man's use has depleted the natural woodland cover of the dale, by allowing little chance for regeneration to take place. Ideally a balance should be maintained between the right numbers of stock and the vegetation, whereby one helps the other. If there are too many sheep, everything gets eaten, and if there are not enough, the vegetation grows up and overwhelms the young saplings and plants, and they get smothered.

In the gills, there are calcite flushes at the side of the numerous waterfalls, amidst the more characteristic acidic rocks of the Lake District. Here different kinds of plants are able to grow together, such as Maiden Hair Spleenwort,

Regeneration by pollarding

Ashness Wood

Columbine, Yellow Mountain Saxifrage, Lady's Mantle and the familiar Cranesbills. It is a combination of gentle purples, yellows and greens, with the fluffy white flowers of the Meadowsweet serving as a backdrop. Overhanging the gill are Bird Cherry and Mountain Ash, typical of a Dales scene. Following the gills down to the valley bottom, we find another change of habitat with more marshy areas, where we are greeted by the strong, musky smell of Bog Myrtle. Here orchids grow alongside Bogbean and Sundew, indicating the presence of the tarn and its wetter surroundings.

Watendlath is a place of contrasts. The three tarns, the tree-lined gills, the heather fells, the patches of woodland and bog areas, make for an intriguing contrast of landscapes. The Nature Conservancy Council, recognizing its potential, has reached an agreement with Dick Richardson to help this balance be carefully maintained. He has to keep his sheep numbers at an appropriate level, so that the land is not over-grazed, and he is recompensed accordingly. Already parts of the dale have been fenced off, so that the traditional broad-leaved woodland is able to regenerate. Oak, ash, birch and sycamore saplings are now being given a chance to mature, against a carpet of different coloured mosses and lichens. As one of the first farms in Lakeland to enter into such an agreement, the Richardsons may be setting a pattern for the future.

It is from these various sources that a modest living is made. The holding not only has to keep life ticking over at Fold Head, but must also maintain Shaun's young family. Despite the uncertainty of the future, his hopes are to carry on where Dick leaves off.
As Shaun says: "It's a grand life . . . if you don't weaken."

He is not the kind to weaken easily. He would like to play his part in caring for the valley, as different generations have done before him. Like his father, his fulfilment lies at Watendlath.

Columbine   *Ash sapling*

Returning home after a sheep gather

Dick Richardson

"Lambing takes place in the intakes"
Shaun squeezes mucus from the mouth of a new-born lamb to enable it to breathe

Fetching home a poorly lamb

Regeneration of broad-leaved woodland

Oak saplings grow towards the light

Dick scans the crags for stray sheep above Langstrath

Going home for clipping

At clipping-time contract workers are brought in to help.
When the wool is off, the sheep are marked with red 'smit'

"We dip t' sheep three or four times a year"

Dock Tarn

Butterwort thrives in the bog areas close by the tarn

"The upper reaches of Watendlath have a sense of wildness about them"

Beyond Watendlath Tarn, Derwent Water and Bassenthwaite Lake can be seen

Ashness Wood

Silage is fed to the suckler cows

Short days, mists lower
Winter sets in

83

"We ruddle tip for t' first ten days"

The cows are brought inside for winter

Winter feeding

Going home

With Margaret

ENNIS
— of —
DEEPDALE

There are only a handful of working farms in Deepdale now, and for the most part these are situated on the gentler western slopes. On the eastern side, where the land rises more steeply, the looming presence of Whernside dominates the tiny dale; here the tell-tale signs of derelict barns and abandoned buildings hint at a past when once there were more hands to care for the place. A third of the way along the valley the back lane deteriorates into a rough track, and few folk choose to live in the remoter parts now.

Beneath the expanse of the open fell, subject to ever-changing moods, numerous tree-lined gills and waterfalls cut across the pasture land, creating a lively patchwork of varying shapes and colours in the valley bottom. It is this typical Dales scene that lies sketched out in the front of Docklesyke Farm, home of Ennis and Herbert Bentham. It is this familiar view that they see each morning from their kitchen window, while Herbert makes their breakfast porridge and Ennis prepares for her day's work

The weather rolls in across the Whernside tops. Scudding cloud and lowering mists frequently conceal the peak's true height and lead the eye up toward the head of the dale, where the land sweeps round to form a circular corrie carved out from the fellside. All too abruptly Deepdale ends. The only clue as to any continuation is a narrow, winding road that manages to find its way up the fell, only to disappear mysteriously over the tops. All round the dale there is a clear dividing line between the richer pasture land lower down and the coarser grazing on the fell. The colour changes from lush green to a combination of soft brown-greys, with only the darker lines of the stone walls to provide contrast. Like pencil lines these divide up the fell into allotments for the different farms, and stamp the mark of human ownership upon the land.

At Docklesyke, the land is kinder and falls away more gently towards Deepdale Beck. Here, on October days, when mists tend to linger in the lower valleys, the sun rises up over Whernside and each indentation on the fell, made by the water runnels, is picked out by slanting light. It lends magic to the place. The farmsteads bask in the morning sunshine, yet they are far from still. Their occupants are early risers and they have already been about their business for some time.

It is among these surroundings that we see Ennis Bentham, in wet or shine, moving purposefully from one field to another, from one barn to the next, going about her daily tasks. Protected from the chill wind by a wool head scarf and an old coat, she moves assuredly, knowing every characteristic of the pasture and each bump or hollow of the fell. Her face is open, her skin smooth and her cheeks reddened from being out in all weathers. When she smiles, her face takes on a slightly mischievous look, as though she knows some secrets from the fell. She claims that the animals sense her womanhood, which would not surprise the onlooker, for her disposition is one of calm and surety. She accepts the pattern of her life with equanimity.

Ennis has lived in Deepdale for all but a few years of her life. Brought up on a farm at the lower end of the dale, she moved away at the age of seventeen, only to return a few years later when she married Herbert and took up residence at Docklesyke. She has lived there ever since. The ownership of small farms is not always a simple business. Partnerships are formed and dissolved owing to the changing circumstances caused by birth, marriage and death. Some children take to farm life and some do not, so arrangements have to be made and re-made accordingly.

Herbert had been in partnership with two other families for many years, until ill-health got the better of them and they split up. The only way Ennis and Herbert were able to carry on working their farm in Deepdale successfully was to ask their younger son Tony to return home to help them. He had been gaining valuable experience by working away on various farms as a stockman since leaving school. However, it is well known that there is little fulfilment in farming unless you work for yourself. At the age of twenty-five he was relieved to have that opportunity; he gladly returned home to Deepdale with his wife Kathleen, and plenty of new ideas and fresh energy to inject into the hill farm.

It is within this closely-knit family unit that Ennis plays her part.
Herbert, being quite a few years older than Ennis, does less of the arduous work as years go by. He spends his time filling in the ministry forms, doing the accounts, and helping out with some of the lighter tasks. The majority of farm work is now shared between Ennis and Tony. It is a mother and son team.

Herbert and Nicola

Nicola with Tony

91

The Benthams have a mixed farm of about one hundred acres of inside land with allotments on the fell. There are milk cows, suckler cows and sheep, but the more stable, regular income comes in from the milk. When Tony returned home he recognised that changes were needed: his enthusiasm was infectious and the family decided to make some improvements to the holding.

"We thought it was about time to bring t' farm into t' twentieth century. Soon we'll be in t' next 'un and we'll have missed out altogether!"

Building work began. They decided that there should be a new silage pit and a proper track for the heavier vehicles to use in bad weather. They also installed a more efficient mucking out system – and a four-wheel bike, electric shearers and feed troughs were bought. These were all time and labour-saving devices designed to help run the farm more easily and effectively.

Tony and Ennis cope with most of the building work themselves, though help comes in the form of a man with a concrete mixer. When he arrives he looks at Ennis in her white breeches and jumper, but she forestalls comment.

"So what do you think to your labour force then?"

"I think we may be pushing it!"

Tony intervenes: "She won't keep you waiting."

And she didn't . . . at least only once. They kept at it all day and were done by eight o'clock at night – the floor of the silo pit had been laid.

The idea of lightening the work-load is so that more time can be spent caring for the stock and carrying out the onerous task of maintenance work. In past years there were many more folk helping on these farms, but there is no longer the money for extra labour now. The four-wheel bike not only saves time but also wear on the legs, so that when the morning jobs are done there is still a readiness for work in the afternoon. Before the bike came along, fodder had to be carried to the stock, and this might involve a good few miles of up and down walking.

The work changes from season to season, which gives some variety to the daily routine. In winter months there are the calves to feed and the fat bulls to fodder with hay and nuts in the bottom shippen; after that it is onto the four wheeler to see to the hoggs and breeding ewes. Meanwhile Tony does the milking, lets the cows out to eat silage, and mucks out. In November time there are tups to ruddle and feed, but both Ennis and Tony do that together for "they're beggars to catch." In spring-time there is little chance of keeping to any routine at all, for it is all hands to the lambing shed from morning till night.

There is little work that Ennis resents.
"It's usually a twelve hour day, though on wetter days it's less. But the work has to be done. It's a bit like being a mother: it has to be your whole life." There is a friendly banter in the farmyard as they go about their tasks.
"You should see her muscles!" Tony shouts across from the milking parlour. "There's not much she can't cope with."
"Women don't get muscles," Ennis retorts. "Look 'ere." And she duly rolls up her sleeve to show off the feminine quality of having strength with no muscle. Ennis is not afraid of giving as good as she gets.

Tony respects his mother's ability, and is grateful for the support she gives him.
"Though we have our own jobs to do, Mother is capable of doing any of them. Mind you, she might not like some . . . but she'll get stuck in when she has to."

Ennis explains: "I'm not keen on tractor work. First time I tried it I lost five pounds in weight in three days. Seat's hard, t' neck aches from craning round, and leg tires from pushing on t' clutch. It has to be done so I do it, but take buck-raking for example, I find it very hard work. You're driving something that isn't stable and occasionally it falls down a hole and tractor comes off t' ground and I don't like getting stuck. But even that you get used to. I like walling – for there's something to see at t' end of it. But then that can be a tough job for a woman to do by herself because of t' weight of t' stones. The big ones are very heavy. But then there are plenty of mighty strong women who aren't afraid of a bit o' work. I could name a few here abouts who would turn their hand to anything. I'm only one of many."

And she is. Ennis is but one example of those many women who work all hours of the day and night, making their own contribution to the up-keep of the hill farms. Among the fells and dales the womenfolk play an essential role in the protection and care of the land. Without them their husbands would find it hard to make a living. Herbert remembers the old saying:

"'A wife will either make you or break you'. Aye, there's a lot o' truth in that."

Not only do the women help with the farm work, they also run households where washing and baking are no light tasks, for the outdoor work produces plenty of muck and creates big, hearty appetites. Combining farm work with house-keeping at times requires the ability to watch dust collect. Priorities have to be got right. In fine weather wall gaps need putting up, hedges need laying, and at the end of the day the back aches and there is not the energy for hoovering and polishing. On wet days there is a better chance of catching up inside, for when the rain teems it is less easy to carry out the maintenance work on the farm.

Given the choice, Ennis would prefer to spend her time with the animals. She enjoys the feel of wool and the exhilaration of the work, and she has recent memories of being house-bound.

"I cared for Herbert's Dad the last three and a half years of his life. Old folks don't like to be left for long – in fact they don't like to be left at all . . . and I believe if you're going to do a job, you do it properly. So someone had to stop in and look after t' old lad and it was mostly me. When I had a sitter I used to go out and do my bit, but if you only go out once a fortnight, you feel your strength going. I began to get so slow, and it got harder and harder for me to do anything outside. I got to going how old folks go. After he died, I started to help again, but it took time to get me strength up. Tony would twine that I was slow, and I would play heck with him! I told him there was no point in rubbing it in."

Now, instead of a grandfather, there are three small grandchildren to look after, and often Ennis has a little one beside her when she feeds the beasts. They like to be out with Grandma. She chatters on and gives them jobs to do which keeps them out of mischief, for children need watching on a farm. However, on occasion, Ennis appreciates her little bit of peace.

Ennis's cousin comes to help

"It's when you've just sat down for a rest at t' end of a long day, and there's a padding of little feet and a shout of 'Grandma', and Grandma's expected to do a bit o' looking after. But I know that it gives Kathleen a chance to get out. The trouble is you can't do much when you've got three young 'uns. You can't stay out for long enough. And that's why, for the time being, it's me that does t' farm work."

Ennis was born in 1935 and has spent all her life on farms. She learned the meaning of the word 'work' when she was eight years old during haytime. In those days, before tractors arrived in the Dales, people had to rely on horses, sleds and rakes, which meant farming was a labour intensive business. But that summer her mother had to have her appendix out, and two weeks later her father had an accident and took the end of his thumb off. Her parents had no choice but to rely upon Ennis and her brother Jack as their labour force. She doesn't forget it. Her mother found a way that she could drag a rake along without hurting her wound, and Ennis remembers how just that little bit of help meant so much.

"But it's good if you're brought up to it. You learn things, and you don't realise you've learned them, for everyone has their share to do."

But times are never easy. Now, every bit of energy goes into building up the farm and making it a viable concern that will provide for two families. Holidays and days off are postponed. They would be a diversion, and cannot be afforded anyway; there are too many other things to spend the money on. What if one of the cows were to get mastitis while they were away? It might not be noticed. No-one who was hired to tend the cattle would care for them the same way that the family does. They could not afford to lose out for the sake of a few days away: so sacrifices are made and the situation is accepted, without question and without complaint.

To Ennis the animals are like her pets.

"When you're dealing with cattle day in day out, they get to know you. They come to see you and pull on your coat, nudge you in t' backside, give you a lick and you pat 'em on t' head – you think the world of them. But as soon as they go out of t' gate down that road to auction, they don't exist. You forget them. You just attach yourself to t' next lot and don't worry."

Ennis does not worry. It is not her nature. As in any job of work, there are plenty of problems and many concerns. "But then everyone has them. If they don't, they invent them."

It is how you cope with them that matters. Ennis and Tony will agree that they make a good team and work well together. They discuss ideas, encourage each other, are not afraid of a hard day's work or a good argument. They know what their priorities are and do their best to keep them.

"We decided right at t' beginning that however short o' money we were, we would always try to eat well. If you are properly fed, you're able to carry on. If you start cutting corners and not filling your tummy, things'll go from bad to worse. They say the belly holds the back up, and that's true."

Ennis, like many Dales women, possesses the quality of acceptance. Whatever life brings to her, she makes the best of it and sees good in it. Her beliefs are simple. If there is shelter, food and warmth, what more is there to want? Except of course something to occupy yourself. And that she has.

"I often feel like that widow woman in t' Bible. You know – the lady that goes for more oil in t' vessel and there's only just enough to make the next batch of bread . . . yes, I often feel like her . . ."

"And the barrel of meal wasted not, neither did the cruse of oil fail."

(1 Kings, Ch. 17)

"In winter there are t' calves to feed"

Fetching hay from the barn

Ennis out on the tops looking for buried sheep

Tony helps with the rescue

Daily chores – mucking out

A calf is let outside to suckle

Tony feeding sheep out on the allotment

Ennis goes from one byre to another feeding the animals

Winter evenings – rug making

With Herbert and the grandchildren

"The four-wheel bike not only saves time but also wear on the legs"

Feeding the ewes before lambing

Lambing-time

The children like to be out with Grandma

Warm water is used to revive a 'starved' lamb

Wet days

Making a concrete road down to the bottom barn

Clipping-time

Haytime

Kathleen stows the bales in the barn

A quiet moment

"I like walling 'cos there's summat to see at t' end of it"

Washing the sheep's faces in preparation for the mule gimmer sales

Ear-tagging before market

A tup is blindfolded to stop it "gadding with t' neighbours' yows"

Feeding the Blue-faced Leicester tups

*At the end of tupping-time, the sheep are
returned to the fell for winter*

Andrew and Ian feed a pet lamb

Haytime – Dentdale

Ben and Lisa bring the cows in for milking – Wensleydale

Elaine milking her goat

Mark helps Ann Hodgson feed her sheep at lambing-time

Robert Cubby – Borrowdale

"All that a young shepherd recognises is a deep desire within himself to raise sheep among the fells with his dog at his side"